Maths Revision Booklet
for CCEA GCSE 2-tier specification

T2

Compiled by Lowry Johnston

Rewarding Learning

Contents

A calculator may be used in these exercises.

Approved/endorsed by CCEA on 30 April 2012. If in any doubt about the continuing currency of CCEA endorsement, please contact CCEA. Whilst the publisher has taken all reasonable care in the preparation of this book CCEA makes no representation, express or implied, with regard to the accuracy of the information contained in this book. CCEA does not accept any legal responsibility or liability for any errors or omissions from the book or the consequences thereof.

Publisher's Note
This book has been written to help students preparing for the CCEA GCSE Mathematics 2-tier specification from CCEA. While Colourpoint Books and the authors have taken every care in its production, we are not able to guarantee that the book is completely error-free. Additionally, while the book has been written to closely match the CCEA specification, it the responsibility of each candidate to satisfy themselves that they have fully met the requirements of the CCEA specification prior to sitting an exam set by that body. For this reason, and because specifications change with time, we strongly advise every candidate to avail of a qualified teacher and to check the contents of the most recent specification for themselves prior to the exam. Colourpoint Books therefore cannot be held responsible for any errors or omissions in this book or any consequences thereof.

Revision Exercise 1a

1 (a) Calculate

  (i) 3^3

  Answer _____

  (ii) $5^3 \times 2^2$

  Answer _____

  (iii) 0.1×0.6

  Answer _____

(b) From the following list of numbers

  12, 36, 17, 44, 56, 27, 80, 69, 84

  write down

  (i) a multiple of 11

  Answer _____

  (ii) two numbers with a common factor 7

  Answer _____ , _____

(a) The shapes below are made from matchsticks. Shape 1 uses 6 matchsticks.

Shape 1   Shape 2   Shape 3

(i) How many matchsticks are needed to make Shape 5?

  Answer _____

(ii) Explain how you worked out the answer.

_____

_____

_____

_____

b) Jen saves her 1p and 2p coins. She has x 1p coins in one jar and x 2p coins in another jar.
  How much does she have in the two jars?

  Answer _____ p

3 Construct a triangle ABC in which AB = 450 m, BC = 750 m and the angle ABC = 70°.
BC is already drawn to scale.

B —— C

4   A boat is at a bearing of 120° from a lighthouse. It is 650 metres from the lighthouse.
Mark the position of the boat on the grid below.
Use a scale 1 cm to 100 metres.

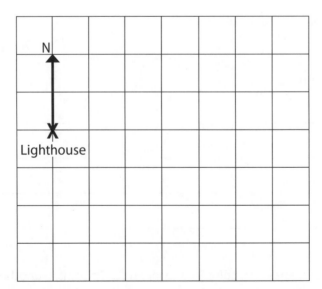

) Calculate

(i) $2^7 \div 2^3$

Answer _____

(ii) 0.3^2

Answer _____

(iii) $\frac{3}{10} + \frac{5}{6}$ giving your answer in its simplest terms

Answer _____

) Write $\frac{3}{8}$ as a percentage.

Answer _____

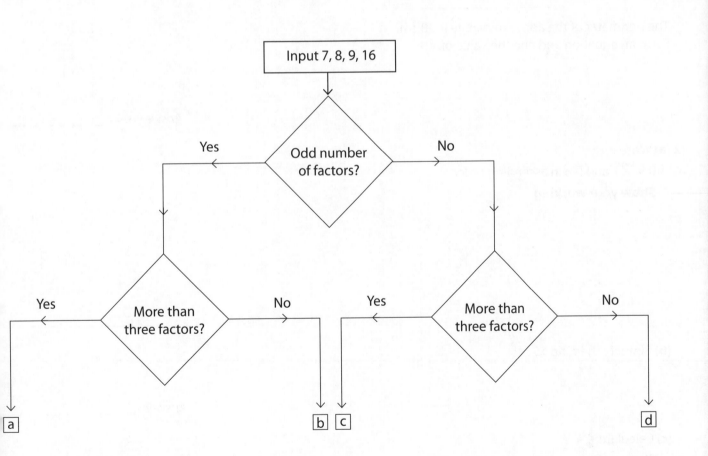

f the numbers 7, 8, 9 and 16 are input, what is output?

a = _____   b = _____   c = _____   d = _____

Revision Exercise 2a

1 (a) Solve

(i) $\frac{x}{5} = 10$

Answer _____

(ii) $2x + 5 = 10$

Answer _____

(b) Expand

$x(x + 3)$

Answer _____

(c)

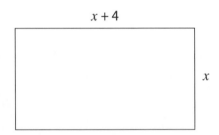

$x + 4$

x

The perimeter of the above rectangle is 28 cm.
Form an equation and find the value of x.

Answer $x =$ _____ cr

2 (a) Write

0.9, $\frac{19}{20}$, and 9% in ascending order.

Show your working

Answer _____ , _____ , _____

(b) Simplify the ratio 15 : 45.

Answer _____

(c) Calculate $\frac{3}{4} + \frac{1}{6}$

Give your answer in its simplest form.

Answer _____

3 A basin is made in the shape of a cuboid. Its length is 30 cm, its width is 30 cm and its height is 20 cm.

(a) How much water will it hold?

Answer _____ cm³

(b) When it is $\frac{3}{4}$ full what is the height of water in the basin?

Answer _____ cm

4 ABD is a straight line and the triangle ABC is isosceles.

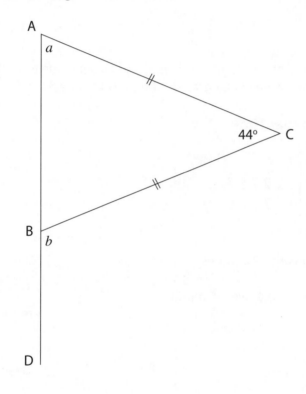

Calculate the size of the angle

(a) *a*

Answer a = _____ °

(b) *b*

Answer b = _____ °

5 Complete the following:

(a)

(i)   (4) ——————→ x 5 ——————→ + 9 ——————→ ( )

(ii)   ( ) ——————→ x 5 ——————→ + 9 ——————→ (44)

(b) Find the next two numbers in the sequence:

7, 2, –3, –8, …. , …. ,

Answer _____ , _____

6 Because of major roadworks, Pat is unsure of how long it will take to get from home to work. The stem and leaf diagram illustrates the times taken during three working weeks (Monday to Friday).

Travel Time

```
4 | 1
3 | 1 2 2 2 5 7
2 | 1 3 7 7 8 9
1 | 9 9
```

Key: 1|9 means 19 minutes

(a) On how many days was the journey to work over 30 minutes?

Answer _____ day

(b) What time was the mode?

Answer _____

(c) What time was the median?

Answer _____

(d) What is the range of times for the journey to work?

Answer _____

(e) Describe what change you would expect in the median and range, if times were recorded for 3 weeks after the road works were completed.

Answer _____

_____

_____

evision Exercise 3a

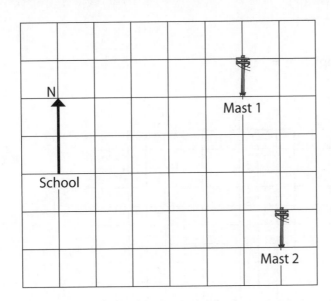

Two telephone masts are put up near a school as shown on the grid above.

Find the bearing of the base of:

a) Mast 1 from the school

Answer _____ °

b) Mast 2 from the school

Answer _____ °

a) Find the cube root of 8

Answer _____

b) Calculate $\frac{5}{12} - \frac{1}{6}$

Give your answer in its simplest form.

Answer _____

3 (a) Complete the table below for the straight line $y = 2x - 3$.

x	−2	−1	0	1	2
y	−5		−1	1	3

(b) Plot the points and draw the graph for $y = 2x - 3$

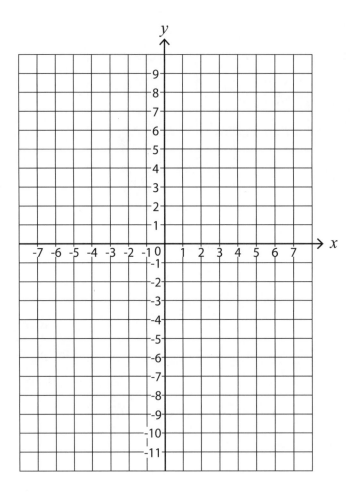

(c) What is the gradient of the line $y = 2x - 3$?

Answer _____

4 36 members of a swimming club were asked what their favourite swimming event was.

The results are shown below.

Backstroke	7
Breaststroke	12
Front crawl	3
Butterfly	8
Freestyle	6

Use the circle below to draw a pie chart to show this information.

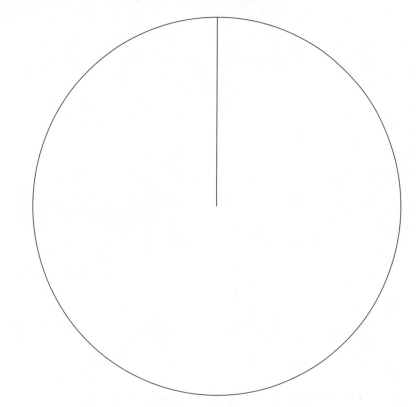

(a)

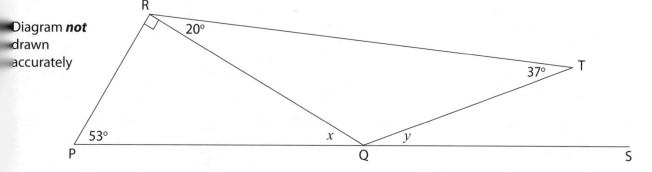

Diagram **not drawn accurately**

PQS is a straight line. Calculate the size of the angle:
(i) x

Answer $x =$ _____ °

(ii) y

Answer $y =$ _____ °

(b) The volume of a cuboid is 168 cm³. The length of the base is 6 cm and the width of the base is 7 cm.
What is the height of this cuboid?

Answer _____ cm

6

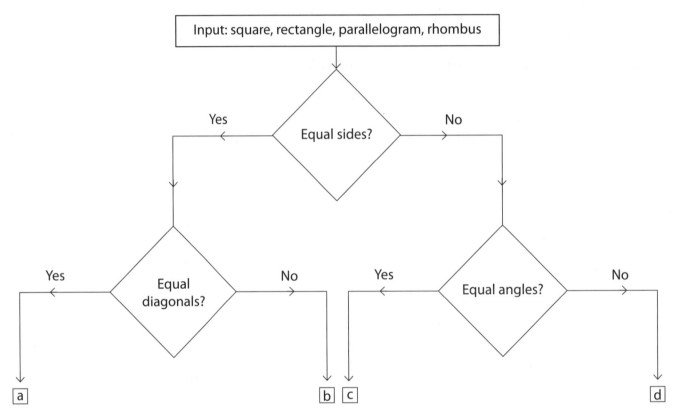

If a square, rectangle, parallelogram and rhombus are input, what shape will be output at:

a = _____

b = _____

c = _____

d = _____

Revision Exercise 4a

1 (a) Calculate

   (i) $(0.1)^2$

                                                    Answer _____

   (ii) the cube root of 125

                                                      Answer _____

   (iii) $3^2 \times 10^3$

                                                      Answer _____

 (b) Which of the numbers 63, 81, 121, 125, 900 is a cube number?

                                                      Answer _____

2 In packets of Mixups there are 36 sweets. The numbers of each flavour are:

   12 toffee
   7 strawberry
   8 orange
   5 coffee
   4 lime

 (a) Use the circle below to draw a pie chart to show this information.

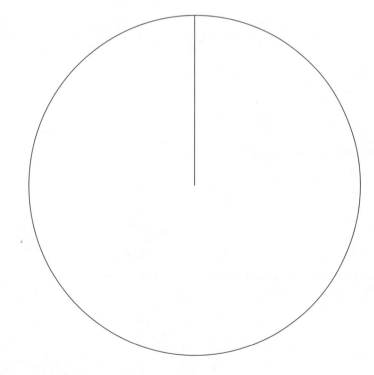

 (b) Why is a pie chart an appropriate way to represent the flavours of sweets in a packet?

   Answer _____

   _____

3 (a) Simplify $4x + 3y + 2x - 5y$

Answer _____

(b) Solve

 (i) $\frac{x}{5} - 1 = 7$

Answer _____

 (ii) $2x + 9 = 1$

Answer _____

4

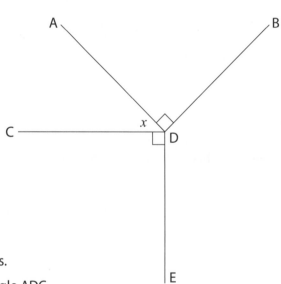

The angles ADB and CDE are right angles.

The angle BDE is twice the size of the angle ADC.

 (a) Form an equation and use it to find the value of x.

Answer _____

 (b) A rectangle is x cm long and 6 cm broad. Its area is $(2x + 32)$ cm².
   Form an equation and use it to find the value of x.

Answer _____

a) Complete the table below for the straight line $y = 3x - 5$.

x	−2	−1	0	1	2	3
y	−11		−5	−2	1	

b) Plot the points and draw the graph for $y = 3x - 5$

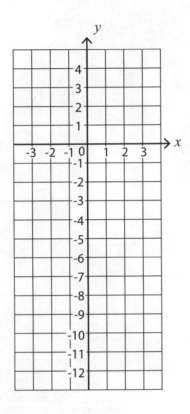

c) What is the gradient of the line $y = 3x - 5$?

Answer _____

6 Cushyair flies to Glasgow and London from Belfast.

Scale: 1 cm = 50 km

What is the bearing and direct distance of

(a) Glasgow from Belfast,

Answer Bearing _____ °, Distance _____ km

(b) London from Belfast?

Answer Bearing _____ °, Distance _____ km

evision Exercise **1b**

a) Calculate:

(i) $1\frac{3}{4} + \frac{3}{10}$

  Give your answer in its simplest terms.

  Answer _____

(ii) $\frac{9}{10}$ of 500 ml

  Answer _____ ml

(iii) $2^3 \times 5^2$

  Answer _____

b) Write out 90 out of 300 as a percentage

  Answer _____

a) Write down the next two terms in the sequence:

  $7, 4, 1, -2, \dots, \dots,$

  Answer _____ , _____

b) Write down the first three terms in the sequence with the nth term given by $n^2 + 7$

  Answer _____ , _____ , _____

c) The perimeter of the rectangle drawn is 36 cm. Form an equation and use it to find the value of x

$x + 7$

x

  Answer $x =$ _____

(a) Factorise
  $x^2 + 9x$

  Answer _____

(b) Multiply out and simplify
  $3(x - 5) + 1$

  Answer _____

(c) Solve
  (i) $5(y - 3) = 20$

  Answer _____

(ii) $2(3x - 1) = 28$

  Answer _____

4 (a) Draw the graph of $y = 2x - 1$ on the grid below.

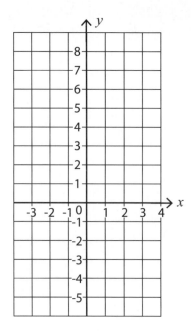

(b) What is the gradient of the line $y = 2x - 1$?

Answer _____

5 (a)

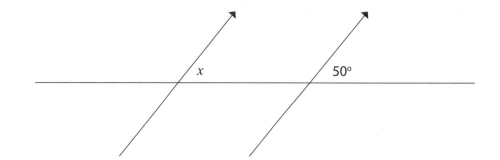

The drawing above shows a pair of parallel lines crossing a straight line.
(i) Write down the size of the angle x

Answer _____

(ii) Give a reason for your answer.

Answer _____

(b)

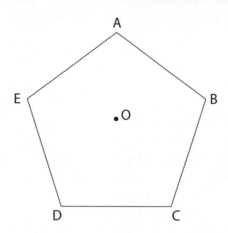

ABCDE is a regular pentagon with centre O.
(i) Calculate the size of the angle AOB.

Answer _____ °

(ii) Explain why the interior angle of a regular pentagon is 108°

Answer _____

_____

(iii) Calculate the size of the angle ADE.

Answer _____ °

Declan is walking along a straight coastal path. From a point X he spots a buoy on a bearing of 058°.
400 m further along the path at a point Y the bearing of the buoy is 300°.
The line XY is drawn below using a scale 1cm to 40 metres.

(a) Use this line and the bearings given to plot the position of the buoy.

(b) Find the shortest distance of the buoy from the coastal path.

Answer _____

X ————————————————————————— Y

Scale 1cm to 40 metres

7 (a) A is the point with co-ordinates (–1, 1) and B is the point with co-ordinates (3, 5)

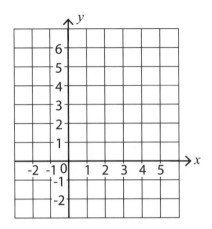

(i) Find the co-ordinates of the midpoint of AB.

Answer (_____ , _____)

(ii) Find the length of the line AB.

Answer _____

(b) Describe how you could test if a dice is fair (ie it will produce the results you would expect).

Answer _____

_____

_____

_____

_____

_____

_____

_____

_____

Revision Exercise 2b

1 (a) Complete the blanks for the function machine.

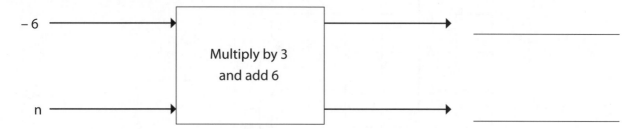

-6 ⟶ | Multiply by 3 and add 6 | ⟶ _____

n ⟶ | Multiply by 3 and add 6 | ⟶ _____

(b) A regular polygon has an exterior angle of $45°$.
Find the number of sides in the polygon.

Answer _____ sides

(c) Write down the nth term of the sequence
7, 13, 19, 25,

Answer _____

2 (a) Write 70 out of 200 as a percentage.

Answer _____ %

(b) Calculate the prime factors of 324. Now write 324 as a product of prime factors in index form.

Answer _____

(c) Calculate and give your answer in its lowest terms.
   (i) $4\frac{7}{12} - 2\frac{1}{3}$

Answer _____

   (ii) $2\frac{1}{4} + 3\frac{7}{8}$

Answer _____

3 (a) Draw the graph of $y = \frac{1}{2}x + 3$ on the grid below.

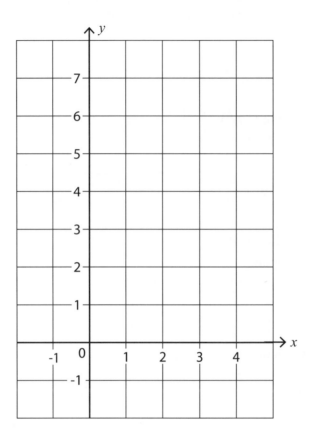

(b) What is the gradient of the line of $y = \frac{1}{2}x + 3$?

Answer _____

4 When phoning an information centre, callers may be put on hold depending on the volume of calls.
For a sample of callers, the length of time on hold is recorded in the table below.

Time (t) in minutes	$0 \leq t < 4$	$4 \leq t < 8$	$8 \leq t < 12$	$12 \leq t < 16$	$16 \leq t < 20$	$20 \leq t < 24$
Frequency	32	20	14	2	3	1

(a) Which class contains the median?

Answer _____

b) Draw a frequency polygon to show the data.

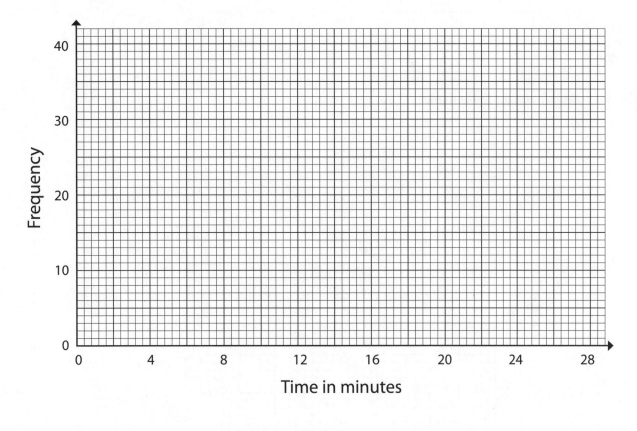

a)

```
      **          ***        ****        *****
      **          ***        ****        *****
      **          ***        ****        *****
                  ***        ****        *****
                             ****        *****
                                         *****
```

Pattern 1   Pattern 2   Pattern 3   Pattern 4

There are 3 rows of 2 stars in Pattern 1 so the number of stars is 3 × 2.
Study the pattern of stars.

(i) How many rows are there in Pattern 9?

Answer _____ rows

(ii) Write down an expression for the **total** number of stars in Pattern *n*.

Answer _____ stars

b) Expand and simplify
$x(x + 2) + 2(x + 2)$

Answer _____

6 Two Judges X and Y awarded marks to ten skaters in a competition.
The marks are as follows

Judge X	18	7	12	3	17	5	1	11	14	7
Judge Y	16	6	13	5	15	4	1	10	15	7

(a) Draw a scatter graph for these marks.

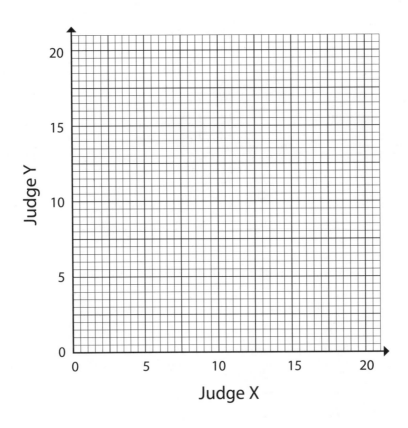

(b) Draw a line of best fit on the scatter graph.

(c) A late entry was awarded 15 marks by Judge X. Estimate the mark that Judge Y may have awarded.

Answer _____

evision Exercise 3b

a) Multiply out and simplify

  (i) $7 + 3(x - 2)$

                                                Answer _____

  (ii) $2(3x + 1) + 3(x - 2)$

                                                Answer _____

b) Solve

  (i) $7(x + 3) = 35$

                                        Answer $x =$_____

  (ii) $4(5x + 2) = 48$

                                        Answer $x =$_____

a) Calculate

  (i) $6\frac{2}{3} + 2\frac{3}{4}$

                                                Answer _____

  (ii) $4\frac{1}{4} - 2\frac{3}{5}$

                                                Answer _____

b) Calculate the simple interest on £300 invested for 2 years at 10% interest per year.

                                                Answer £ _____

(a)

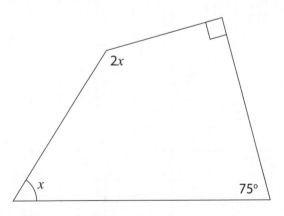

Form an equation and use it to find the value of x.

                                                Answer $x =$_____ °

(b) (i) Find the perimeter of the triangle below. Write your answer in its simplest form.

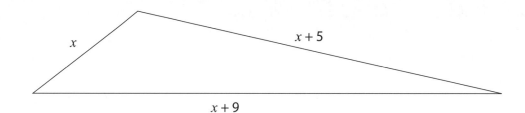

Answer _____

(ii) The perimeter of this triangle is 35 cm. Form an equation and find the value of x.

Answer $x =$ _____ cm

(c) Write down the nth term of the sequence
5, 10, 15, 20, . . .

Answer _____

4 The latitude and temperature at seven locations in the northern hemisphere are recorded in the table below.

Latitude	20	5	58	45	32	15	54
Temperature (°C)	35	42	20	28	31	37	22

(a) Draw a scatter graph for this data.

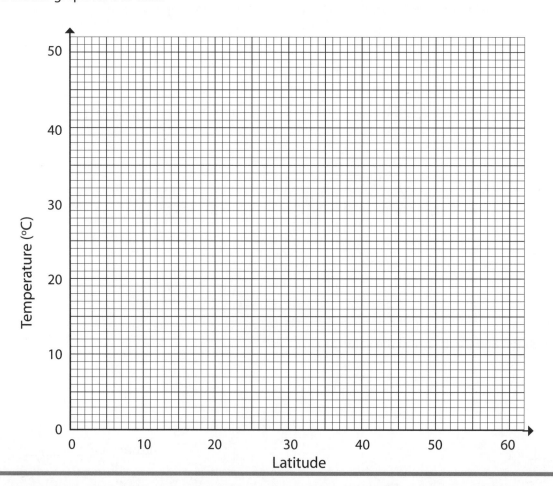

b) Draw a line of best fit on the scatter graph.

c) Use your line of best fit to estimate the temperature at the location where the latitude is 40^0.

Answer _____

a) Arlene weighed her suitcase before going to the airport. To the nearest kg, it weighed 20 kg.
What is the least weight it could be?

Answer _____

b) Declan is putting up a track for a blind to fit exactly between the two edges of a window. He measured the length between the window edges to the nearest cm and cut the track to fit.
Explain why it may not fit.

Answer _____

_____

_____

a) Write as a product of **prime** factors.
  (i) 30

Answer _____

(ii) 105

Answer _____

b) What are the common **prime** factors?

Answer _____

c) Find the HCF (higest common factor) of 30 and 105.

Answer _____

Revision Exercise 4b

1 (a) In Eastwood School 380 pupils took canteen dinners each day.
When healthy diet meals were started, the number of pupils taking canteen dinners increased by 40%.
How many more pupils took canteen dinners each day?

Answer _____

(b) Mrs Jones wrote a cheque to pay Eastwood school £27.50 for her son's dinner tickets.
Complete the cheque to show what she should have written.

```
┌─────────────────────────────────────────────────────────────────────┐
│                                                                       │
│  NORDEN BANK                                            98 – 76 – 54   │
│                                                                       │
│  Norden plc, The Mall, Mainton NB3 2AX           Date _____   │
│                                                                       │
│  Pay  _____                             │
│                                             ┌─────────────────────┐   │
│       _____  £ │                   │   │
│                                             └─────────────────────┘   │
│                                                           R. Jones    │
│                                                                       │
│       _____            R Jones                  │
│                                             _____          │
│                                                                       │
│   ⑈00000 ⑆⑈  98⑈ 7654⑈   123456 78⑈                                 │
└─────────────────────────────────────────────────────────────────────┘
```

2 (a) Factorise

(i) $9x + 6$

Answer _____

(ii) $x^2 - 7x$

Answer _____

(iii) $x^2 + x$

Answer _____

(b) Find the nth term of the sequence
5, 8, 11, 14, . . .

Answer _____

mpack collects and delivers parcels. A random sample of 100 parcels is selected and their weights recorded. summary is shown in the table below.

Weight of parcel (P kg)	Frequency
$0 \leq P < 5$	38
$5 \leq P < 10$	25
$10 \leq P < 15$	10
$15 \leq P < 20$	15
$20 \leq P < 25$	8
$25 \leq P < 30$	4

a) Which class contains the median?

Answer _____

b) Draw a frequency polygon for the data.

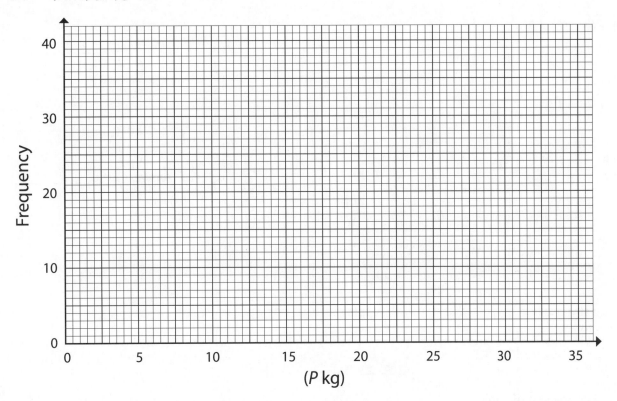

(P kg)

(a) Which of the following fractions is nearest to $\frac{1}{5}$?

$\frac{3}{20}$, $\frac{6}{25}$, $\frac{9}{40}$, $\frac{11}{40}$

Show your working

Answer _____

b) Calculate

(i) $\frac{2}{5}$ of £60

Answer £ _____

(ii) 20% of £170

Answer £ _____

(c) Siobhan's dog eats $\frac{3}{4}$ tin of dog food per day. What is the least number of tins she should buy to last 1 week?
Show your working

Answer _____ tins

5 (a) Multiply out

$x(x^2 + 3)$

Answer _____

(b) Expand and simplify

(i) $5(2x + 3) - 2(3x - 5)$

Answer _____

(ii) $x (x - 2) + 4 (x - 2)$

Answer _____

(c) Solve

(i) $7x - 8 = 3x$

Answer $x = $_____

(ii) $8x - 13 = 3x + 7$

Answer $x = $_____

6 (a)

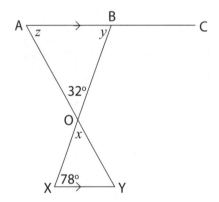

ABC is a straight line
parallel to XY.

Calculate the size of angle

(i) x

Answer _____

(ii) y

Answer _____

(iii) z

Answer _____

(b) P and Q have co-ordinates $(-3, 1)$ and $(5, 5)$ respectively.
Find the midpoint of PQ.

Answer (_____ , _____

(c) Find the length of the line PQ.

Answer _____

Revision Exercise 1c

1 (a)

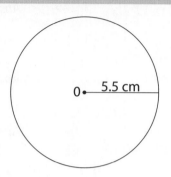

0•—— 5.5 cm

Find the area of the circle of radius 5.5 cm.

Answer _____ cm²

b)

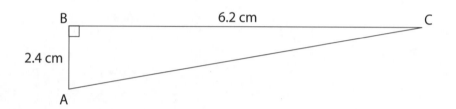

B ———————— 6.2 cm ———————— C

2.4 cm

A

ABC is a right angled triangle.
AB = 2.4 cm and BC = 6.2 cm

Calculate:
   (i) the area of ABC

Answer _____ cm²

   (ii) the length of AC

Answer _____ cm

Use trial and improvement to find the value of x between 4 and 5 satisfying the equation $x^3 - 4x = 81$
Give your answer correct to 1 decimal place.

Answer _____

3 (a) Write 60 as a product of its prime factors.

Answer _____

(b) Find the LCM (lowest common multiple) of 60 and 42

Answer _____

(c) Find the HCF (highest common factor) of 60 and 42

Answer _____

4 (a) Calculate correct to 2 decimal places.

(i) $1 \div 0.8$

Answer _____

(ii) $\sqrt{3.62^2 + 6.41^2}$

Answer _____

(b) If $4x^3 = 108$, what is the value of x?

Answer $x =$_____

5 The number of minutes each plane is late taking off at Belfast International Airport is recorded for a sample of flights.

Time (t) in minutes	Frequency	Mid-value
$1 \le t < 9$	3	5
$9 \le t < 17$	17	
$17 \le t < 25$	28	
$25 \le t < 33$	31	
$33 \le t < 41$	16	
$41 \le t < 49$	9	

Calculate an estimate for the mean number of minutes that planes are late taking off.

Answer _____ minu

6 Two shops have a sale on TVs.

(a)

```
┌─────────────────────────────┐
│       A B Dig Electrical     │
├─────────────────────────────┤
│                             │
│          SALE               │
│                             │
│  Digital Ready 32 inch TVs  │
│                             │
│           £660              │
│                             │
│    We pay your 20% VAT      │
│                             │
└─────────────────────────────┘
```

How much would the TV cost if VAT had been included?

Answer £_____

(b)

```
┌─────────────────────────────┐
│       R S Tel  Electrical    │
├─────────────────────────────┤
│                             │
│          SALE               │
│                             │
│    Digital Ready  TVs       │
│                             │
│   15% off the marked        │
│          price              │
│                             │
└─────────────────────────────┘
```

The marked price of an identical 32 inch Digital TV is £750.

Which shop is the cheapest and by how much?

Answer   Shop _____ by £ _____

Revision Exercise 2c

1 Use trial and improvement to find the value of x between 3 and 4 satisfying the equation $x^3 - 7x = 28$

Give your answer correct to 1 decimal place.

Answer $x =$ _____

2 (a) Ken invests £3600 for 3 years at 5% per year simple interest.

What is the total amount after 3 years?

Answer £ _____

(b)

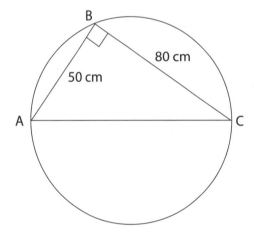

AC is a diameter and ABC is a right angle.

Calculate the circumference of the circle drawn above.

Answer _____ c

3 A store buys dresses for £80.00 each. They are then priced so that the store makes a 40% profit on each dress sold.
Customers with a store loyalty card are given 2% discount off the selling price.
How much does a customer with a store loyalty card pay for **one** of these dresses?

Answer £_____

he pocket money given to a sample of children aged between 9 and 11 years old is shown below.

Pocket money (£P)	Frequency
$1 \leq t < 3$	1
$3 \leq t < 5$	14
$5 \leq t < 7$	27
$7 \leq t < 9$	39
$9 \leq t < 11$	6

alculate the mean pocket money.

Answer £ _____

a) Calculate
$$\frac{2.9 \times 4.5^2}{6.3 - 1.8}$$

Answer _____

) Calculate $\sqrt{7.41^2 - 2.16^3}$

Answer _____

.) The volume of a cylindrical paint tin is 5000 cm³.
   How many litres is this?

Answer _____ litres

) The height of the tin is 28 cm.

Calculate:
(i) the area of the base of the tin,
Give your answer correct to the nearest cm²

Answer _____ cm²

(ii) the diameter of the tin.
Give your answer correct to the nearest cm.

Answer _____ cm

(c)

M Y Cash 42 Uptown Road Kinore KN4 3PQ	Bank Account Statement Your overdraft limit is £250	West Bank 40 High Street Kinore KN1 7GG

Account Number 00120030

Date	Transaction Details	Payments Out	Payments In	Balance £
8 February 08	Balance brought forward			87.22
9 February 08	Bank Credit – Hut & Co.		309.62	396.84
10 February 08	Direct Debit – Phone Co.	65.98		330.86
14 February 08	ATM Cash Withdrawal	200.00		_____
15 February 08	Direct Debit – Electric Co	74.35		_____
17 February 08	Direct Debit – Car Loan	109.00		_____
20 February 08	Debit Card – Asha	24.47		_____
21 February 08	Lodgement		80.00	3.04
22 February 08	Bank Credit – Hut & Co		309.62	312.66
	Balance carried forward			312.66

Complete the balance column of the bank statement to find between which dates the balance in the account was below zero.

Answer Between _____ and _____

ANSWERS

Answers

Revision Exercise 1a
1 (a) (i) 27 **(ii)** 500 **(iii)** 0.06 **(b) (i)** 44 **(ii)** 56, 84
2 (a) (i) 26 **(ii)** multiply by 5 and add 1 **(b)** $3x$ pence
3 Accurate construction
4 Accurate positioning of boat on grid
5 (a) (i) 16 **(ii)** 0.09 **(iii)** $\frac{17}{15}$ **(b)** 37.5% **(c)** 53000
6 $a = 16$ $b = 9$ $c = 8$ $d = 7$

Revision Exercise 2a
1 (a) (i) 50 **(ii)** $2\frac{1}{2}$ **(b)** $x^2 + 3x$ **(c)** 5
2 (a) 9%, 0.9, $\frac{19}{20}$, **(b)** 1 : 3 **(c)** $\frac{11}{12}$
3 (a) 18000 cm³ **(b)** 15 cm
4 (a) 68° **(b)** 112°
5 (a) (i) 29 **(ii)** 7 **(b)** -13, -18
6 (a) 7 **(b)** 32 minutes **(c)** 29 minutes **(d)** 22 minutes **(e)** Both to get smaller

Revision Exercise 3a
1 (a) 068° (± 2°) **(b)** 109° (± 2°)
2 (a) 2 **(b)** $\frac{1}{4}$
3 (a) -3 **(b)** graph accurately plotted and drawn **(c)** 2
4 Pie chart angles 70°, 120°, 30°, 80°, 60°
5 (a) (i) 37° **(ii)** 20° **(b)** 4 cm
6 a = square b = rhombus c = rectangle d = parallelogram

Revision Exercise 4a
1 (a) (i) 0.01 **(ii)** 5 **(iii)** 9000 **(b)** 125
2 (a) 120°, 70°, 80°, 50°, 40° **(b)** Pie chart is used to show the contents of the **whole** packet of sweets.
3 (a) $6x - 2y$ **(b) (i)** 40 **(ii)** -4
4 (a) 60° **(b)** 8 cm
5 (a) -8, 4 **(b)** Accurate plotting of points and drawing of graph. **(c)** 3
6 (a) 035° (± 2°), 160 km (± 5km) **(b)** 131° (± 2°), 475 km (± 5km)

Revision Exercise 1b
1 (a) (i) $2\frac{1}{20}$ **(ii)** 450 ml **(iii)** 200 **(b)** 30%
2 (a) -5, -8 **(b)** 8, 11, 16 **(c)** 5.5 cm
3 (a) $x(x + 9)$ **(b)** $3x - 14$ **(c) (i)** 7 **(ii)** 5
4 (a) Accurate drawing of $y = 2x - 1$ **(b)** 2
5 (a) (i) 50° **(ii)** corresponding angles are equal **(b) (i)** 72° **(ii)** angle OAB and angle OBC are isosceles triangles; OBA and OBC are both 54° so ABC = 54° + 54° = 108° **(iii)** 36°
6 (a) Using the given bearings, locates buoy where lines cross **(b)** 120 m
7 (a) (i) (1, 3) **(ii)** 5.66 **(b)** Toss it a large number of times. Record the scores. Check that each score occurs about the same number of times.

Revision Exercise 2b
1 (a) -12, $3n + 6$ **(b)** 8 **(c)** $6n + 1$
2 (a) 35% **(b)** $2^2 \times 3^4$ **(c) (i)** $2\frac{1}{4}$ **(ii)** $6\frac{1}{8}$
3 (a) Accurate drawing of $y = \frac{1}{2}x + 3$ **(b)** $\frac{1}{2}$
4 (a) $4 \le t < 8$ **(b)** (2, 32), (6, 20), (10, 14), (14, 2), (18, 3), (22, 10) joined with straight lines
5 (a) 11 **(b)** $(n + 1)(n + 2)$ **(c)** $x^2 + 4x + 4$
6 (a) Points from table accurately plotted **(b)** Line of best fit **(c)** 14